Written by Nicki Swann

Illustrated by Ashley Reynolds

ISBN 978-1-62806-297-7   (print | paperback)

Library of Congress Control Number 2020919787

Published by Salt Water Media
29Broad Street, Suite 104
Berlin, MD 21811
www.saltwatermedia.com

Cover and interior illustrations by Ashley Reynolds

DEDICATION

To Poppop Lloyd
for your ever-present love and support

**Published with the encouragement and support of Anne Altvater and the team of Campbell's Lane Farm
… where anything is possible!**

22862 Dover Bridge Road
Preston, MD 21655
www.campbellslanefarm.com

Psst! It's me ... Pogo!
See me over here?
I'm the one with my halter
tangled around my ear.

I can't get it off.
I've tried and I've tried.
It's so embarrassing I decided to hide.

I know I should ask for help but I don't.
I never ask for help so I won't!

I'll figure this out. I have a thought.
I'll have to hurry before I get caught.

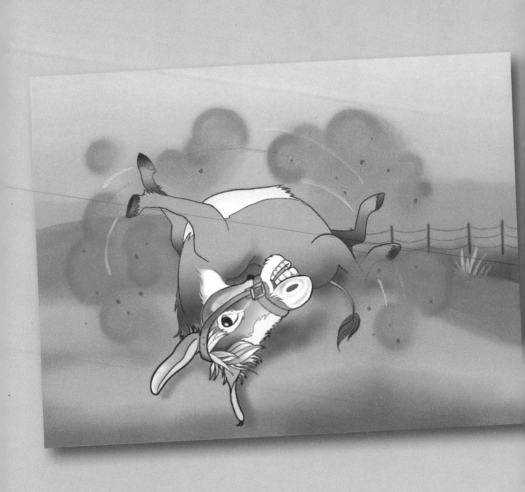

I will plop down on the ground,
roll back and forth,
around and around.

Well, that made it worse.
Now it's tangled real tight.
That thought didn't work,
but this one just might.

I'll put the metal hook on the fence,
then pull real hard. It's common sense!

"Lollipop, please get out of the way."

"Hold on, Pogo!
I have something to say!"

"Lollipop,
I really don't need your advice.
I'll just hook this right here..."

I've been shocked by the fence,
with the halter still on my ear.
Pretty soon I might not be able to hear!

This is my last shot,
but I'll do it with ease.
I'll gallop so fast
it flies off in the breeze.
I can do this, I already know.
Okay, ready, get set,
spin your hooves and let's go!

I'm sad to let the story end this way.

Guess I'll give up
and go eat some hay.

No!
Pogo never gives up, not at all!
I guess the only thing left to do
is HEE HAW!!!

That got their attention!
Yup, they're looking at me.
Here they come to my rescue!
My ear is free!
It seems all I needed
was my donkey yelp.
Now I know it's okay to ask for help!

ACKNOWLEDGEMENTS

First I would like to thank God for blessing me with the ability to achieve this dream. He created me with such an imagination and a passion for writing and helping others. If this book touches at least one soul in a positive way I will feel accomplished.

I owe so much of my achievement to the team at Campbell's Lane Farm. Anne Altvater has believed in me and pushed me for so long to reach for the stars and show the world that anything is possible. She created a place for me to spend each day doing what I love and convinced me to write and share my stories with the world. Linda Mastro has been my coach on this adventure. She has encouraged me and gotten me out of my box. I have learned so much from her and she helps mold my creations in such a loving way. This book would not be possible without her hard work and dedication. Jennifer Fox reminds me that this is something I was born to do. She has read my work throughout the years and her reactions make me feel like a superstar. I am thankful for all the support and courage she has given me.

This book truly comes to life because of illustrator Ashley Reynolds. She created the illustrations exactly how I imagined them when writing the story. Her ability to capture the personality of both the humans and the animals blows me away. The passion she puts into her work combined with her fun spirit brings tears to my eyes each time I see one of her beautiful works of art.

Thanks to everyone at Salt Water Media. It's not every day you find a place that makes you feel like home. I am excited to be working with someone like Stephanie Fowler and this team that is so close to my roots.

A special thanks from my heart to my family. My parents, Laura and Randy Swann, have been reading my poems since I was old enough to write them. Every holiday included a card with words created in my heart, bounced around in my mind, and written down with whatever I could use to express myself. They always treasured my words and I'm so thankful they still do today. My grandparents, Lemmie and Renee Swann and Lloyd and Brenda Bayliss, are my rocks and inspirations, passing so many talents down to me. They have come to every special event throughout my life with such pride on their faces. I am so excited to experience the publication of my first book with them.

- Nicki Swann